Tumi to the Rescue

Tumi
to the
Rescue

The Tempting Cupcakes

Dr. Cindi Mendoza

Illustrated by Cindi Robinson

Palmetto Publishing Group
Charleston, SC

Tumi to the Rescue
Copyright © 2020 by Dr. Cindi Mendoza
All rights reserved

First Edition

Printed in the United States

ISBN-13: 978-1-64990-105-7
ISBN-10: 1-64990-105-4

BOOK REVIEWS

. . . .

"I recommend this book because it takes you on adventures. It is funny and teaches you more about GOD. Hope you like it too!"

Amanda D – age 9

"This book was amazing!! I really enjoyed reading this book because it taught me how the Lord knows the future and the past. This book is great for children who need to know that God is with us always."

Sophie C.- age 10

I dedicate this book to my Lord Jesus Christ. Thank you for the privilege and honor of serving you and your kids. May your WORD go forth into all the world to make disciples of all nations. Use me Lord! Choose me!

I dedicate this book to my husband and my boys, Lorenzo, Kenzie, and Diego. Thank you for loving and honoring me. You are my treasures.

I dedicate this book to my very special students at Victory Christian School in Tulsa, OK. Thank you for the honor of teaching you. I know the Lord has great plans for you.

I dedicate this book to all of my girls and boys at Cindi's Hope. May you be lights that draw millions into HIS Kingdom.

CHAPTER 1

· · · · · · · · · · · · ·

The Golden Girl

I jumped off the school bus and waved goodbye to my friends, being careful to leap over the giant mud puddle that was just waiting for me to splash in. *I made it*, I said, smiling to myself. I had thought that would make a great big splash...but Mom would not have been very happy with me if I did that.

"Bye, Grace! Bye, Sam! Have fun this weekend," I shouted.

"Bye, Tumi," they shouted back as the bus drove off down the dirt road, swerving to avoid more big mud potholes. The bus splashed in a few as it went down the road.

I started walking toward my house. *Thank goodness it is Friday and I do not have class tomorrow,* I thought. *I like school, but I really love the weekends. I'm going home to put on my superhero outfit and ask the Lord where I am needed. It's like an adventure every weekend. I wonder what we will do together next. Maybe I can save someone's life!* I skipped up to the gate of the compound as the guard opened it for me. I walked into the house and greeted Auntie. An auntie is a Kenyan maid who helps take care of the kids when their parents are at work. The auntie does the laundry, cooks, and just kind of minds her own business... most of the time. Auntie was busy chopping and dicing food for dinner.

"Hello, sweet Tumi," she greeted me. "I've cut up some yummy fruit with yogurt for a snack. Why don't you eat after washing your hands?" I crinkled my nose. I really wanted cookies and chocolate syrup and a candy bar. Chocolate was my favorite, but

Auntie didn't usually give me sweets at snack time. I didn't want to complain, but, well, I DID.

I know I am to do everything without complaining and arguing. Geez, that's kinda hard, I thought. *EVERYTHING? Do EVERYTHING without complaining. How about some things? I think I can do SOME things without complaining. Like, eat chocolate candy bars at snack time. I can do that every day. No problem. But do everything? That is HARD.*

I know the Holy Spirit was talking to me. He reminded me of a song I had learned. I held my tongue with two fingers and started singing it: "From Philippians 2, verse 14. Do eeevvvvvery-thing without complaining, do eeeevvverything without arguing, so that you may become blameless and pure chilllldren of God. Without complaining. Without arrrrgggguing, do do do do everything without complaining." I continued singing the song as I held my tongue...that tongue could get me into a lot of trouble. Now I knew why the Sunday school teacher always had us hold it. *Ha ha ha,* I laughed to myself.

"Tumi," Auntie said, "please, please do not do that without washing your hands. What are you trying to say anyway? I cannot understand you when you hold your tongue."

"Yes, Auntie." I thought this was a lot of practice. Wash my hands, don't complain...this was hard work. It's not hard to complain. It is HARD to obey.

I finished washing my hands and sat at the table to eat my snack. Maybe, if I pretended it was a chocolaty snack, somehow it would be. I thanked Jesus for the delicious snack and took a big bite, pretending I was eating fruit with chocolate sauce on it. Yum, yum!

CHAPTER 2

· · · · · · · · · · · · ·

Jane and the Cupcakes

That same afternoon, Jane walked home from her day at school...*Walking home can be so fun!* Jane thought as she purposely jumped into each passing mud puddle. With each new puddle, she tried to make a bigger splash. She wasn't wearing her mud boots, but man, those puddles just were smiling at her to jump on in.

"Jane," Auntie said, exasperated. "Why are you doing that? Everything, including YOU, is completely covered in mud. Can you please try to walk around the puddles?"

Jane looked at Auntie and jumped with both feet right into an oncoming puddle. The splash was so big it got her and Auntie muddy. *Wow! NICE*, Jane thought.

"Jane, I said to stop," Auntie said, grabbing her hand and pulling her to the side of the road where there weren't any more puddles. They came to their house, and Auntie opened the gate. Jane followed her up to the house and took her muddy shoes off outside.

The aroma of cakes, chocolate cream frosting, mandazis, custards, and cupcakes with candies in the middle came wafting through the air. The house smelled like heaven. Jane felt her mouth start to water as soon as she walked into the house. Auntie must have been baking all day.

Jane went right to the table where the desserts were cooling. Her mouth hung open as she took a deep breath, inhaling their sweet, yummy goodness. *Yummmmmmy! Auntie is the best baker ever. I really hope I can bake as well as she does when I'm big.*

There were chocolate cookies with white, soft powdered sugar sprinkled on top. Frosted queen cakes with small chocolate pieces inside and sprinkles on top of the creamed cake were beautifully displayed on the table...yellow ones, brown ones, blue ones, pink ones. Jane's eyes were mesmerized...and she was imagining eating ALL of them. She started to reach out to take one of the cupcakes, but right before her hand reached it...

"Jjjjjannnnnne," Auntie said, "those are for your sister's party this weekend. You may NOT eat them now."

"Oh, of course, Auntie." Jane replied. "I know I'm not allowed to eat sweets after school. Mom said to have some *uji*." Yuck. Jane realllly, reallllllly disliked *uji*. She was thinking, *I'd rather eat dirt! That stuff is terrible. I am pretty sure that dirt does taste better; in fact,* uji *might be liquid dirt...it has little crunchy things in it.* She pondered eating dirt for a snack...but then thought she might get a stomachache.

"Go upstairs and change your clothes, Jane," Auntie said as she walked outside to hang the laundry on the line.

"Okay." Jane watched her go out the back door. *Here's my chance. Ha!* She was so excited. *Auntie will never notice if I just take one.* Then, as Jane was looking at them, she wondered, *Which one do I take? I can't even decide. Okay...maybe one of EACH. That is a brilliant idea. One of each kind. HA.* That was it. Auntie would never know if one of them was missing. One chocolate cake with sprinkles—coming right up. Plop...right into her gaping mouth. *Oh, oh, oh, the one with the candies,* she thought as she barely finished chewing. She grabbed the candy one and began stuffing it into her mouth. *Yes, the candy one... yum. Let me just get a cream one.* Just as Jane was going to take her finger across the frosting, she heard a shriek.

"JAAANNNEE MUGO!" Jane jumped because the shriek was so piercing. She thought something had died, it was so loud and shrill.

Auntie took hold of the wooden spoon and started swinging it. She held onto Jane's arm as the wooden spoon hit the back of Jane's hind side. "Sorry, Auntie! Sorry, Auntie!"

Auntie pulled Jane outside and gave her one more loud smack on her backside as the thunder boomed overhead. "You stay outside in time-out!" she exclaimed, slamming the door and latching it.

Jane was really scared because the thunder was so loud. *Maybe even God is mad at me,* she thought. She started crying really hard and telling Him she was sorry. "Lord, I'm so sorry I ate all those desserts. I am so sorry that I didn't obey Auntie. I know I am supposed to do my homework and not come down into the kitchen to steal food. Lord, I am so sorry for being naughty and not listening." She was crying so much that it was hard to tell if she was wet from tears or rain.

CHAPTER 3

· · · · · · · · · · · · ·

Golden Socks

I skipped upstairs to my room to change out of my school uniform. I began praying and asking the Holy Spirit where He wanted me to go and who needed His help this weekend. I loved this part of the weekend the most. Helping other kids was just awesomesauce, maybe even awesome CHOCOLATE sauce. Hee hee. I just cracked myself up.

If I didn't have school during the week, I could help kids all day long and I might never have to do spelling again. *Maybe there's a special superheroes school. I bet spelling isn't even at that school! Spelling isn't needed in helping people. Oh, I am complaining again,* the Holy Spirit reminded me. *Sorry, Lord. Bless spelling...*I giggled.

Walking into my room, I remembered this song I had learned on Sunday and started humming..."Way maker, miracle worker, promise keeper, light in the darkness. My God, that is who you are." I loved singing to the Lord even though my brother thought I sounded like a chicken when I sang. I think he meant another bird. Birds sing nicely. Chickens? Um...I was not so sure. I hummed and put my school clothes away and took out my superhero uniform.

It was so nice. Some of the Sudanese aunties who sewed downstairs in their extra room had made it for me. It had golden socks, a shiny golden cape, a black leotard and tights, and a golden belt. As I put it on, I recited each of the special pieces of armor my mom had taught me. The breastplate of righteousness: this protected my heart and all my important organs. The belt of truth: we should always speak the truth in love. Jesus is truth. I put on my golden boots. The boots took me places to share the gospel of the Kingdom of God. My cape...um. I looked at myself in the bathroom mirror. The cape was a super-duper extra cool piece that the aunties made me. It made me feel as if I could fly. It was made from a shiny golden fabric. I ran around the room, making the cape fly out behind me long and wavy. Then I stopped...breathing hard from running in circles down the hall and into the bedrooms. I grabbed my golden sword that fit into my belt of truth. It wasn't a super long one, but it was long enough to fight and kill the enemy.

Swoosh, swoosh. I practiced a few stabbing motions in the mirror just to make sure I could use it quickly from my belt. *Pretty good*, I thought. I wondered when I would get to use the sword as I put it gently back into its sheath. I kept humming and thought, *Lord, who will you send me to who needs you right now?*

Just as I was saying the last words, I had some pictures go through my mind. It's kinda like I'm seeing a little commercial on TV, but it's just me in my room. I heard my Sunday School teacher call it a vision. I already have vision. I went to get my eyes checked, and the doctor said I have 20/20 vision. So I don't really know what he's talking about. I just know I can see something like a small commercial, but I don't have the TV on.

I stopped humming and paid really good attention. I didn't want to miss what the Lord was showing me. In my commercial vision, there was another little girl down the street. The girl was younger than me—maybe only five or six years old. Her auntie was hitting her with a wooden stick and left her outside as it began to rain. "Lord," I prayed, "where do I find her, and what is her name? How can I help her?" I concentrated on listening with my heart to the Holy Spirit as I walked down the stairs in my golden outfit. I felt especially invisible and invincible with it on. Something about the golden cape and the golden uniform made me really take to heart all the memory verses I had practiced. "I will never leave you nor forsake you." "A thousand will fall at my side, ten thousand at my right hand, but it will not come near to me."...I grabbed an umbrella as the wind and the rain started to pick up.

CHAPTER 4

· · · · · · · · · · · · ·

Tell the Rain to Stop

I continued listening to the Holy Spirit in my heart. Sometimes this is difficult. I remember my Sunday school teacher telling me that when Jesus said, "Listen," that meant to hear what He was saying "and DO" it. Sometimes we just hear but do not actually do it. That is the hard part: obeying.

I left the house quickly and ran down the road. I was careful not to splash too much on my golden socks. I had gone only a few blocks before I saw the same roof that was in my commercial vision. A black iron gate wrapped around the property.

The rain started to come down harder. I was getting cold as the wind and rain were blowing on me. This rain needed to stop. It was starting to get my golden socks dirty. I was sure the little girl, Jane, I saw was cold as well.

Hey! I remembered a story we learned last week. Jesus was in the boat with the disciples. Jesus was asleep while there was a terrible storm. Some of the disciples were fishermen—men who knew how to fish and were on the water a lot. Those guys were a bunch of scaredy-cats though. They were so scared they thought they were going to die. Jesus kept right on sleeping. Ha, that Jesus. Taking a nap during the storm. He wasn't worried one. little. bit. One of the guys went over to Jesus and woke him up. The disciple Peter said to Jesus, "Don't you care if we die?"

Jesus got up and said "Be still" to the storm.

Listen means hear and obey. Even the wind and the waves listened and obeyed Jesus. So cool! Hey! Just like that, Jesus made the rain, wind, and big waves stop just by commanding them. *Well, I* thought, *umm, if Jesus is the Way Maker and Miracle Worker, and the Holy Spirit is in me, I should try telling the wind and rain to stop too.* "BE STILL," I commanded with authority. The wind stopped blowing. The rain slowed to a drizzle and then to nothing. I looked at amazement at the sky above me. Wow! The Word of God is so real. Why don't people believe it?

I stepped over a puddle and reached my hand inside the black gate to unlock the door. I entered the compound and prayed there weren't any dogs around. Often in Kenya each compound has a few dogs. "Jane, Jane," I called. I knew she was around the back hiding because I heard the Holy Spirit tell me. As I came around the corner, I spotted Jane huddled up under a tree in a corner with her face in her hands, crying and asking God for help. "Jane, the Lord has heard your cry. He loves you so much and he doesn't want anyone hurting you or leaving you outside in the storms. He knows how afraid of the thunder you are.

"My name is Tumi. That's short for Tumaini which means Hope. The Lord sent me to help you out of the rain and cold. Come with me. Let's be friends and stick together until your mom comes home from work." Jane reached up and hugged me really tightly. She was crying and shaking and was very, very wet and muddy.

I was so sad for Jane but also so very happy the Lord had shown me where to find her and how to help her. I didn't want the auntie to come outside and find us. I heard the Lord saying we needed to go. We needed to walk around the house, away from the windows, and toward the gate to exit the compound. *Ummm, I am not sure I heard that right. Do we need to exit the compound, Lord?* I pulled on my ear. I know HE wasn't speaking words in my ear, but I couldn't hear well. Usually, all little girls and boys should stay inside. Mom always says, "Don't leave the compound!"

A compound has a house in the middle of a big yard with a wall surrounding it. No one can just come in and knock on the front door. The person would have to stay on the street and knock on the gate. It isn't safe for boys and girls to leave their compounds without their mom or dad or auntie.

Jane was really wet and scared. *Lord, I don't know what to do,* I thought. *I am not so sure about what I am hearing.* I stuck my finger in my ear and wiggled it around. Maybe I could hear more clearly. Maybe some rain fell in there and was blocking the signal. Then I saw what the Holy Spirit wanted me to do. Right at the edge of the compound, connected to the gate, was a little house. Sometimes a guard slept in there at night to protect the house. We needed to go in there and get out of the cold. The Lord always knows what's best. Sometimes we just need to look around and see what He is telling us to do. Or clean out your ears like I do.

Just as we were nearing the small little house by the gate, the rain and wind began again. I think my dad would say, "It's going to rain cats and dogs." We went running into the small house, holding hands as thunder clapped over our heads.

CHAPTER 5

• • • • • • • • • • • • • •

Raising from the Dead

"Jane, come with me." I grabbed her hand and walked real determined-like. "Let's hurry over here. I know what will make you feel better and you won't be scared anymore. Let me tell you a story about our God. Do you know that He hears you when you cry? Do you know he keeps all of your tears in a bottle? That's amazing, isn't it?" *He saves my tears...I thought of that as I was telling little Jane. God, you are such a wonderful daddy. No wonder one of your names is Baba. You don't like it when we cry.*

"Our God is so wonderful...let me tell you a story about Him. Once, a long long time ago, there was a little girl. Now, the little girl was a slave girl in Syria. She didn't even have her mom and dad anymore. She was the maid to a very important captain's wife. A maid is kind of like an auntie, but you don't get paid. One day the slave girl overheard the wife and Captain Naaman talking about his disease. He was really sick. There wasn't any medicine available for him. The girl knew that the Lord was able to heal any disease or sickness. In fact, there isn't anything He can't cure. So the little girl boldly went forward out of the closet where she was hanging the clothes and said, 'Excuse me, sir, there is a prophet from my country in Israel who can heal you. If you go and see him, he will pray to the Lord my God for you and you can be healed.'

"Now the captain didn't know what to think. Of course, small slave girls never spoke to him. His wife really loved this little girl from Israel. She was so kind and obedient. She always had a smile on her face and helped his wife with joy. The little girl was well liked and admired in his home. Something told the captain he should listen and look for this prophet in Israel. The captain smiled kindly at the girl. 'Thank you for considering me and for taking such good care of my wife. How do you know he can cure me?'

"'Well,' said the slave girl, 'when I lived at home, the prophet, Elisha, brought my friend back to life after he died. His mom and my mom were very good friends. We used to play together all the time. But one day my friend was working in the field with his dad. He got a terrible headache and died the same day. I was so sad.'

"'My friend's mom sent for the prophet right away,' the slave girl explained. 'She did not start crying and screaming as other Jewish ladies do. She believed the man of God would pray for her son, and she was right. When the prophet came later that day, he went upstairs where my friend was lying.'

"'You know'—the slave girl looked at the captain intently—'the prophet did a strange thing. He was praying quietly to God under his breath. Then he lay down, covering the boy's body with his own, eye to eye, hand to hand. It seemed very strange to me. I thought the prophet would just tell the boy to be healed and arise. Maybe the boy's body was cold because he had already been dead most of the day while we waited for the prophet to arrive. I am not sure. I just remember thinking it was very strange. BUT my friend was completely healed. More than healed, he was dead, then ALIVE. I knew from that time on that my God can do anything. I just need to obey and believe.'"

CHAPTER 6

· · · · · · · · · · · · ·

Riding to Israel

"'That is some story,' the captain said, smiling at her.

"'Sir, it's more than a story—it's a miracle. I know my God can heal you too.'

"'Would you be willing to go and see the prophet with me then?' the captain asked her.

"'Of course! I would love to go and see my beautiful Israel. I know the Lord my God will heal you. When can we leave, sir?'"

I stopped the story and looked at Jane closely. "Jane, you know what? The captain rode his horse all the way from Syria to Israel looking for Elisha the prophet. Naaman, the captain, had to travel at least two weeks by horse to get to Israel. That's a long way to go to see the doctor, huh?"

"Two weeks on a horse? I don't even like riding in the car to go visit the doctor," Jane said. "He must have been pretty sick to ride his horse that far."

"He was pretty sick," I told her. "This disease didn't have medicine to cure it, and it only gets worse and worse. It makes your fingers and toes come off—your nose and ears too. The captain probably had gloves on his hands and boots on his feet to try and hide the disease from other people."

"What? Yuck!" exclaimed Jane. "That's a terrible sickness."

"The captain traveled with a lot of people from Syria to Israel. He was the CAPTAIN. That means he had a lot of men that went with him. The captain had two hundred men that rode in teams of ten," I explained.

"Ten, twenty, thirty, forty, fifty, sixty, seventy, eighty, ninety, one hundred," Jane counted and then stopped. "I don't know what comes after a hundred," she mused. "Two hundred?"

"Well, not exactly," I said. "You have to start over again. One hundred ten, one hundred twenty, one hundred thirty, one hundred forty, one hundred fifty, one hundred sixty, one hundred seventy, one hundred eighty, one hundred ninety, two hundred." We both shouted together and then laughed.

"Syria and Israel weren't friends either," I went on to tell Jane. "Those two countries fought a lot. So the captain rode his horse for two weeks with his troops into enemy territory to find Elisha. The captain had to have been pretty determined and brave to get healed. And I think he must have really believed the small slave girl. That's one of the best parts about our God. He always gives us hope. The captain had hope that if the God of Elisha could raise the dead, he could heal his skin also.

"What about the slave girl? Did she go with the captain?" Jane asked.

"She came too. Can you imagine? I don't know how long she had been a slave to the captain's wife, but I am sure she missed her mom and dad in Israel."

"That must have been an adventure for sure. I don't know if I would have liked it," Jane said as she looked up at the ceiling of the small room we were in. "I wonder," Jane said, "if she was thinking, just maybe, maybe she would see her mom?"

CHAPTER 7

· · · · · · · · · · · ·

A Vision

"You know what the funny part of this story is, Jane?" I told her as I pulled her up by her hand and led her outside. The rain had stopped and the sun was shining. I plopped down on the steps and pulled her down with me. "It really is amazing. The Lord told Elisha that Naaman was coming EVEN before he arrived at Elisha's house. Elisha SAW them arriving."

"Even before?" Jane asked. "So I can know things before they happen? Like when Auntie is coming so I don't get caught eating the desserts?"

"Wellllll, not exactly," I replied, giving her a side-ways glance. "It's not so you can be sneaky—it's so you can give other people warnings or assistance. When you see something, but it isn't really there, that's called a vision. A vision is like a dream, except you are awake and your eyes are open. Elisha could see things with his spiritual eyes. Think of spiritual eyes like special goggles for swimming. You can see all kinds of things very clearly underwater, but with-out them, they're all blurry and shadowy. That's how it is for most people. But not Elisha or me. We can see things most people can't. SUPER COOL, huh?"

"What? Wow!" Jane exclaimed. "I want to do that."

"Kind of like you today. God told me where you were and where you were hiding. I could see you hid-ing when it started to rain, but I was still at my house.

"God told Elisha that Naaman was coming with a group of soldiers and he wanted to be healed from his disease. Elisha continued his work, even after the Lord told him this big important captain was coming to see him and be healed. Elisha sent his ser-vant out to meet the captain and give him instruc-tions on how to be healed.

"Hey, I have an idea!" I squealed. "Let's go and see them," I told Jane.

"How?" Jane asked. "I thought you said they lived a long time ago. How can we go and visit them? Are you sure we can leave the compound? We might really get in trouble then."

"Hold my hand and close your eyes. Jesus, please let us go to see the captain and the slave girl. We want to see Naaman get healed."

We opened our eyes and were sitting on a rock. All around us were trees and shrubs. It was dry and rocky with lots of dirt. It looked like a wilderness. It was not very green, but rockier and with lots of dirt.

Ohhhhhh! What did I just do? I thought. *I know Jesus says if we do not ask Him, we will not receive. I never thought I could go back and see something in the Bible, though. I have never done that before...*

We looked up from the rock we were sitting on and saw what must have been Elisha's house in the clearing. We could see a big group of men riding upon horses and a little girl riding with one of the soldiers.

CHAPTER 8

· · · · · · · · · · · · ·

The Healing

"Look! That must be the captain, and there's the slave girl. I wonder what her name is. Let's go over and see them." I glanced down at my clothes, thinking I would look really obvious in my golden superhero uniform. I was hoping I wasn't still wearing my golden boots and socks. I might really make a scene in Israel dressed as a superhero. To my relief, I noticed we both were wearing dresses and had scarves over our heads.

We walked toward the group of men on horseback. I could see what must have been Gehazi, Elisha's assistant, speaking with the captain. The captain was easy to spot. He had a helmet with red feathers sticking out all across the top. He kind of looked like a rooster head. Ha! I tried to keep my laugh inside. Why would someone dress like a rooster? He looked silly. The captain also had on a breastplate. Hey! He had on the armor, like the armor of God. I was getting more excited as I watched them.

Then, the captain was mad. "Why would I come all this way to go into the dirty Jordan River?" the captain angrily retorted to Gehazi.

"What's going on?" Jane asked. "Elisha didn't come out and talk with him?"

"No, remember? The Lord told Elisha why the captain was coming to see him and what the solution was to cure him. Elisha just instructed Gehazi to go and tell him. Elisha never even meets the captain."

The captain and his secretary, Gehazi, continued standing together. Gehazi said, "Go and wash seven times in the Jordan River."

"Jordan River!" the captain almost yelled angrily. "That river is brown and disgusting. My country, Syria, has beautiful rivers and lakes. Surely, this is a ridiculous solution. Why did I ever listen to a young slave girl?"

The captain turned his horse and all the team around. He was very annoyed. He had just ridden for over two weeks to see this prophet AND the prophet didn't even have the good manners to come out and greet him. "Oh, these people in Israel," he huffed. As the captain was storming past the slave girl on his horse, she called out to him. "Sir, surely if the prophet had told you to do something very diffi-cult, you would have done it because you are such a brave soldier. Even if he had told you an expensive price, you would have paid. Just because he asked you to do something very simple, please do not con-sider it a small thing. Healing comes through our faith and our obedience to the Word. If the prophet is giving you instructions to dip in the Jordan River seven times, let us go and do it. My mom used to say nothing is more important than obedience."

Exasperated yet encouraged by the young girl's boldness to speak to him in front of his men and the servant, the captain agreed. "Where shall we go?" he asked Gehazi.

Gehazi hurriedly grabbed his donkey and threw the blanket on top. "I will show you."

With Gehazi leading the way, all the men, along with the slave girl, headed off in the direction of the Jordan River. After a few hours of traveling, they neared the stream. It should have been a large river. The slave girl could understand the captain's dismay and disappointment about dipping in there. It was dirty water, and it looked as if there could be snakes in all those reeds that grow along the bank. One of the men gathered the horses and the donkey as the captain walked toward the bank and started removing his outer garments. He had lots of extra clothes on for battle. As he removed his gloves and the stockings on his feet, the slave girl, Tumi, and Jane could see some of his toes and fingers were missing. They could see the disease eating up his skin and traveling up his arms and legs. Leprosy was a terrible sickness. During the time when the captain lived, there wasn't any cure. Usually, people with this disease had to live very far away from others because no one wanted to be near them. They didn't want to get sick.

The slave girl watched as the captain slowly started walking toward the water just wearing his thin undergarments. All his armor, all his boldness, strength, and power had been left on the banks behind him. It was as if the Heavenly Father were whispering, "Not by might, nor by power, but by my Spirit."

We continued watching and counting. The captain had to walk pretty far into the river because it was shallow. *I hope there aren't any snakes*, I thought. Farther and farther he walked. Finally, when he was about chest deep, he squatted down. Holding his breath, he plunged all the way underwater. We wondered if he could swim...He came up. ONE. The captain looked at the girl and Gehazi. He looked at his hands, then went back under. TWO. He came up again. He looked as if he might be praying. I wondered what he would say to the Creator of Heaven and Earth. THREE. FOUR. FIVE. SIX. He came up the sixth time looking up to heaven and smiling. SEVEN! He came bounding out of the water.

His skin was glowing. The skin looked like a baby's skin I had seen before leaving for this trip. Wow!

Not only was his skin beautiful, but his hair had also grown back fully and was a beautiful brown. Looking beyond his muscular arms, my eyes rested on his hands...beautiful, strong, with formed fingers and nails. Where there used to be some stubs (no fingers at all), new fingers, toes, and nails had appeared. The Lord had caused his skin to be cleansed and even his hair to be restored. What a miraculous God! He IS the Way Maker, Miracle Worker!

CHAPTER 9

· · · · · · · · · · · · ·

Salvation to All Who Believe

"Jane, look. All the soldiers are taking off their armor. Yikes! The men are removing their clothes. They are going to get into the Jordan River too. The Lord wants not just one person saved and healed, Jane—He wants the ENTIRE company of soldiers to believe upon HIM." We turned our eyes as the men were rushing to take off all their armor, gloves, and boots. Clothes were flying everywhere.

The little slave girl was clapping her hands and dancing all around. She started waving a scarf that

had been on her head and sang. We listened intently to hear what she was saying.

"Shhh, she is singing." She sounded much better
than I do...definitely not a singing chicken.

"I love you, O Lord, my strength.

The Lord is my pillar, and my

fortress, and my deliverer;

My God, my rock, in whom I

take refuge;

My shield, and the horn of my

salvation, my high tower.

I will call on the Lord, who is

Worthy to be praised,

And I will be saved from my

Enemies."

Jane looked over to where the company of men
were dipping themselves into the water. "Tumi, I can
see those men with scars on their bodies—as they
go into the Jordan, as they pray and praise the God
of Heaven and Earth, their skin and bodies are being restored. The God of Israel is alive!" All the men
who had followed and served with Naaman in battle rushed into the Jordan River. What a miraculous

God the Israelites had. They wanted to worship Him as well.

The captain came over to the Israelite girl. "Thank you. Thank you for sharing with me that obedience to the God of Heaven and Earth always brings the best results. Would you like to stay here with the prophet? I am sure he can show you where your family is." Handing her some of his supplies, the captain asked Gehazi to take her home to Samaria.

The young girl was so excited—she wrapped her small arms around his waist and thanked him. Of course she wanted to go home, but more importantly, she never imagined that the Lord would use her to lead the captain of the Syrian army and all his men to the Lord. She couldn't wait to tell the prophet and her mom and dad. She had been so sad that she had been taken from her home, and now she saw how faithful and loving God was to her. He hadn't just taken her from her parents—He allowed her to lead the entire company of soldiers to the Lord. Wow!

Jane and I looked at each other and hugged. Wasn't He so good? Naaman got healed, the men in the company got healed, and the little girl got to go home to her mom and dad. We hugged each other as we jumped up and down, rejoicing in the goodness of God. Yahoooooo!

Suddenly, one of the soldiers looked over at us. With eyes as big as saucers, we both realized we needed to get back home ASAP.

"We need to pray, Tumi," Jane whispered.

Grabbing hands and squinting our eyes shut, we prayed together. "Lord Jesus, please take us back to Jane's house now." We felt a rushing wind just as we heard one of the soldiers yelling for us to come to them.

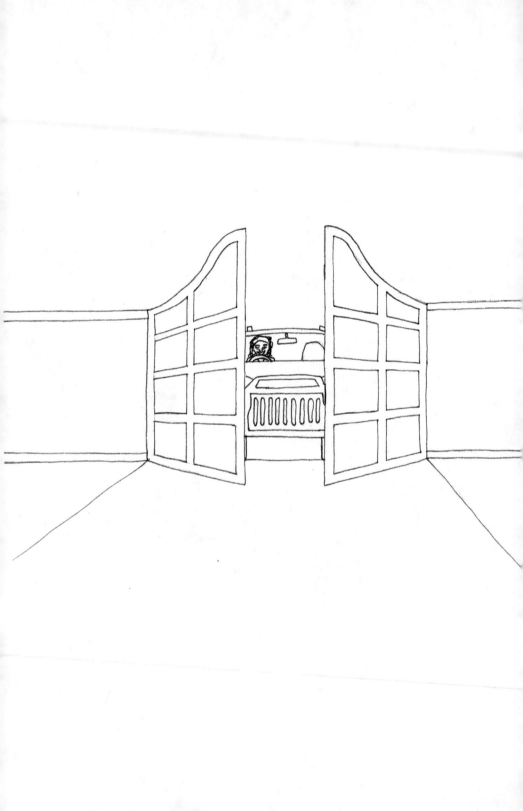

CHAPTER 10

· · · · · · · · · · · · · · · ·

Mom Comes Home

The wind stopped blowing. We slowly opened our eyes to find ourselves outside Jane's gate, back in our own clothes. The sun was shining brightly. Just then, Jane's mom's car came down the dirt road. She was arriving home after work. Both Jane and I were so glad her mom was home. Now Jane wouldn't need to go back into the house just yet to meet the auntie.

"Hi, girls," Jane's mom smiled. "What are you do-ing out here? We always stay inside when we aren't with an adult." Jane's mom honked the horn of the car and waited for the auntie to come and open the big gate. We heard the keys rattling on the inside as the big lock was undone and the gate opened. The auntie looked at us in shock and embarrassment as Jane's mom was peering angrily at her from inside the vehicle. Jane's hair was still notably damp from being in the rain.

Jane's mom slowly pulled the car into the driveway as Auntie closed the gate. *Oh no*, I thought, *now what's going to happen?* I don't usually talk with adults in my golden costume.

"Mommy, Mommy," Jane cried as she ran to her mom's car while she parked the vehicle. "I am so glad you are home. My friend Tumi was telling me a great story about a captain and how God healed him."

"Let's go inside, Jane, and get you out of these damp clothes. Tumi can come too," Jane's mom added. I could tell she was looking at my superhero uniform out of the corner of her eye. I just smiled my big happy smile and followed them into the house. Maybe Jane's mom needed to hear about Jesus also.

"Do you know," Jane went on to tell her mom, "God loves it when we obey? This captain was even healed from his skin problem. At first he did not want to obey. He had taken his whole army to come and see the prophet and thought he would get healed. The prophet told him to go dip his entire body in this really dirty river. Gross! I don't like getting into dirty water either. That seemed like such a silly thing to do to get healed. I know I would not have believed that man. Why would anyone get into dirty water to get clean? That is just plain silly. Just silly!

"Mommy, a little slave girl reminded him that it was an easy thing to obey. Why do I not want to obey sometimes?" Jane paused...tapping her foot. "Well, that's easy. I just don't want to. He reminds me of...me," Jane concluded while making a face. "I did not want to listen to Auntie today. I just wanted to eat all the sweets when Auntie told me they were for Sister's birthday."

Mom was looking at Jane with a surprised expression. First, she knew that Jane loved to eat sweets, but more surprising was that she knew that she was not obeying.

"What happened when the captain obeyed what the prophet said to do?" Mom asked Jane.

"He was HEALED. Mom, what a miracle! You know, his skin wasn't just made clean—he even got back new toes and new fingers. They grew BACK." Jane was staring and wiggling her fingers and toes. "Mom, I didn't know you could grow new fingers and toes."

CHAPTER 11

· · · · · · · · · · · · · · ·

The Truth

"You can NOT grow new fingers and toes," Mom said. Even Mom had forgotten that part. When somebody had the disease that the captain had, there wasn't any medicine for it. "That disease is called leprosy," Mom said. "Now we have medicine for it, but it won't make your fingers and toes grow back. Jesus really is a miracle worker, isn't He?"

"You know," I said, "if the captain hadn't obeyed Elisha, the prophet, he would have died. I think obeying is so very important."

Jane was still looking at her fingers and toes. Mom was staring at both of us. "Ummm, would one of you like to tell me why you were outside the gate?" Mom asked.

"Well, umm, I, I saw my new friend, Tumi, and thought we would go play," Jane said, looking at me.

My eyes grew as big as saucers. We couldn't lie after all we had learned today, I thought. I cleared my throat loudly.

Jane looked down again, and then she said to her mom, "That's not right...I just met Tumi today. She found me outside after Auntie had spanked me with the ugali spoon for eating a lot of desserts for Sister's birthday party tomorrow. Then she made me sit outside in a time-out. It started to rain really hard and I went to hide in the corner so she couldn't find me. I was mad at her and I was afraid because of the thunder.

"I, I..." Jane was trying to decide if she wanted to lie some more or tell her mom the truth. She really wanted to lie. But with me standing beside her, she thought, *Tumi will KNOW I am lying.* Even if she could fool her mom, she couldn't fool me. There was something about my golden belt that made her want to tell her mom the truth, even though she knew she would probably get in even MORE trouble.

Jane told her mom the whole story. She didn't leave out any of the details or the desserts she ate. Then, Jane went over to Auntie and asked her to forgive her for disobeying and eating her delicious desserts.

I knew there was something very important that Jane needed: Jesus and the power of the Holy Spirit. "Jane, you chose to do a hard thing by asking for forgiveness for disobeying. Jesus loves you and died for you on the cross to pay for all the wrong things we do. He says if we ask, He will come into our hearts and live with us forever. He will give us the Holy Spirit, who will comfort, guide, and help us always, like a faithful friend who is always with us. Would you like to ask Jesus to come into your heart?"

"Yes! Yes! I want to know Jesus and learn to listen to the Holy Spirit. What do I need to do, Tumi?" Jane asked.

"Naaman was healed because he humbly trusted in God's way to be cleansed from his leprosy.

You can be made clean from your sin by trusting in God's way of forgiveness and everlasting life. The Bible says, 'For God so loved the world that He gave His one and only Son, that whoever believes in Him shall not perish but have eternal life,'" I shared. I just loved that scripture.

"Jane, pray with me," I instructed as we bowed our heads and closed our eyes. "Jesus—I know that you made me and want me to obey you with all my heart. I know I have disobeyed and wanted to be my own boss. I have thought and done things against your directions. I am sorry. I know that you gave up your life to save me from these sins and make me your child again. I accept your promises and ask you to please save me now and forever. I ask that you give me the gift of the Holy Spirit to be my helper. Amen."

Squealing with joy, we hugged each other, knowing we would be longtime friends.

"Tumi, thank you for coming over today and spending time with Jane. I am glad she has such good friends like you. Would you like to take one of these chocolate cupcakes home? They are filled with peanut butter candies."

"Would I ever! YES, with a capital Y!" I exclaimed. "Chocolate is my favorite."

I hugged Jane goodbye and took a big bite out of my chocolate cupcake as I skipped out the door.

How To Make Jesus The LORD of Your Life

God is not holding your sin against you. He sent Jesus to the cross in your place, so you would not have to pay for you sins, your lies, your stealing, your disobedience. Jesus paid the sin debt for you. But, just as if I am giving you a present, you have to receive it; you have to accept it.

The price has been paid, but it is not automatic. You must choose to accept what He did for you and receive Him as your personal Savior and LORD. If you have never done so, choose Jesus now. Repent, (confess, turn back) of your sins and pray this prayer. When you do, the power of God will make you a new creation in Christ Jesus. Say:

Heavenly Father, in the Name of Jesus, I present myself to You. I pray and ask Jesus to be LORD over my life. I believe it in my heart, so I say with my mouth that Jesus has been raised from the dead. This moment I make Him the LORD over my life. Jesus, come into my heart. I believe at this moment that I am saved. I am a child of the Almighty God! I am a Christian!

Scripture references: John 1:12, 3:16, 6:37, 10:10, 14:6, 16:8-9, Romans 3:23, 5:8, 10:9-10, 13:2, 2 Corinthians 5:17, 19, 21.

How To Be Filled With the Holy Spirit

After Jesus was raised from the dead and before He ascended into heaven, He left us this promise: "You shall receive power when the Holy Spirit comes upon you. And you shall be My witnesses... throughout the world" (Acts 1:8). The Holy Spirit is the One who fills us with power for our Christian walk and to do the works of Jesus (John 14:12).

God has already sent his Holy Spirit. He came to the earth on the day of Pentecost (Acts 2). Now it is up to you to receive Him into your life.

Once you are born again, you can receive the power of the Holy Spirit just as you received Jesus – by faith in God's WORD. All you must do is ask

Him. Jesus said, "If you then, being evil, know how to give good gifts to your children, how much more will your heavenly Father give the Holy Spirit to those who ask Him?" (Luke 11:13). The Holy Spirit will empower you with God's own power! You need His power working in you – ask Him now.

My heavenly Father, I am a believer. I am Your child, and You are my Father. Jesus is my LORD. I believe with all my heart that Your WORD is true. Your WORD says that if I will ask, I will receive the Baptism of the Holy Spirit, so in the Name of Jesus Christ, my LORD, I am asking You to fill me to overflowing with Your precious Holy Spirit. Baptize me in the Holy Spirit, your spirit without measure. Because of Your WORD, I believe that I now receive the Holy Spirit, and I thank You for it. I believe that the Holy Spirit is within me, and by faith I accept Him. Now, Holy Spirit, rise up within me as I praise my God. I fully expect to speak with other tongues as You give me the utterance.

Scripture: Luke 11:9-13, John 14:10, 12, 16-17; Acts 1:8, 2:4, 32-33, 38-39, 8:12-17, 10:44-46; 19:2, 5-6. 1 Corinthians 14:2-15, 18, 27. Ephesians 6:18; Jude 1:20.

Appendix

Chapter 1

Phil. 2:14: "Do everything without grumbling or arguing."

Chapter 3

Eph. 6: The armor of God.

Heb. 13:5: "I will never leave you nor forsake you."

Ps. 91:7: "A thousand may fall at your side, ten thousand at your right hand, but it will not come near you."

Chapter 4

Mark 4:35–41: Jesus calms the storm.

Chapter 5

Ps. 56:8: "You keep track of all my sorrows. You have collected all my tears in your bottle. You have recorded each one in your book."

2 Kings 5: Naaman is healed.

Chapter 8

Zech. 4:6: "Not by might, nor by power, but by my Spirit."

Chapter 9

Ps. 18:1–3: "I love you, O Lord, my strength. The Lord is my pillar, and my fortress, and my deliverer; My God, my rock, in whom I take refuge; My shield, and the horn of my salvation, my high tower. I will call on the Lord, who is Worthy to be praised, And I will be saved from my Enemies."

Chapter 11

John 3:16: "For God so loved the world that he gave his one and only Son, that whoever believes in him shall not perish but have eternal life."

New International Version (NIV)